MAKING OF A MINX

CREATION OF THE MINX

The year is 1953. A young, scruffy boy in a red and black jumper reigned supreme over the pages of The Beano. But that young boy and thousands and thousands of readers were about to meet a girl that could rival the menace.

Also in 1953, one of the most exciting and formative cartoonists in the British comics industry was starting to make a name for himself in The Beano… Leo Baxendale. In 1952, the Preston-based artist had been so inspired by the verve and energy in Davey Law's Dennis the Menace strip that he sent samples of his work to the Beano office. That same year, he had his own strip running in the comic - yes, he was that good! The character was called Little Plum and it was so popular that George Moonie, Beano editor at the time, resolved to use Baxendale on a second strip.

Moonie was very keen to build on the anti-authoritarian streak that was starting to become very popular with Beano readers. To this end, he went down to Preston to discuss characters with Baxendale. What Moonie really wanted was to capitalise on both the popularity of The Beano's brightest star, and Baxendale's admiration of Dennis the Menace. Therefore, what Moonie proposed to Baxendale was the creation of a character who was the female Dennis, as he explains in a letter dated 2nd September, 1953:

Dear Mr Baxendale

Now that that Booster is well in hand I would like you to try out another character, this time a little girl who should come pretty close to Booster in her outlook on life. We'll call her The Minx.

There are two themes enclosed and these will show you the general line to adopt in this series. I'll be glad to have your suggestions for the character whenever you like.

Yours

(G Moonie)

MINXING!

BEANO

Moonie wanted this female menace to mirror Dennis as much as possible. She would have a black beret instead of Dennis's mop of black hair, black skirt instead of black shorts but would wear the distinctive red and black striped jersey which he described in another letter dated 5th September, 1953:

> Herewith the Minx. I like your character. She will take a trick alright, and if the series goes colour the open locks will get a splash of red. This is in keeping with the character and that old saying that you never know what a red-head will do.
>
> One other point is the positioning of the mouths. There is a tendency to push these to one side of the face in an abnormal manner. I think you'll find that the same effect can be got by keeping fairly close to realistic positioning.

Moonie also wanted Minnie's storylines to be a similar format to Dennis's. Much like the now legendary Menace, Minnie's adventures surely did drive parents, teachers, in fact all stuffed-shirt authority figures, totally up the wall. Initially shadowing Davey Law's work, Baxendale soon moved away from imitation and began creating his own personal style, even going so far as only using scripts given to him by D.C. Thomson staff as starting points for his own stories. Moonie's feedback to Baxendale on 17th September, 1953, said:

> Your ideas are still rather wild and with an element of slapstick but I don't mind how many you shove in to me. There is always something to be gained from them.

Where Dennis used brawn to get his way, Baxendale wanted a different route for Minnie, as he said in an interview with the Telegraph newspaper:

" **Characters such as Minnie the Minx used violence, but were not defined by it. I realised as I drew her adventures that what drove her was an intensity of will. This was an Amazonian warrior, a street-fighting woman, but I never showed her hit another child. Where would be the comedy in that? Minnie's fighting techniques – employed against armies of boys – and her inventive demolishing of misguided careers officers and headmasters, would have needed intricate choreography to replicate in real life. "**

This instance of replicating real life was something that was very important to Baxendale, and as he went further into developing Minnie, he developed a new style of language in the comics – moving away from the stuffy and stiff speech balloons of old fashioned comics.

He created dialogue that was more colloquial and that actually sounded like the way children would talk. In this way, Baxendale was influenced by the quippy banter in radio comedies like Tony Hancock's and Max Wall's Hoopla and it paid off big. As Baxendale puts it:

'One day, just after I had moved to Dundee, George Moonie said to me, 'This is the kind of thing we like.' I walked over to George's desk and looked over his shoulder, expecting to see a brilliant bit of drawing. To my surprise, George was pointing at a speech balloon in one of my Minnie the Minx sets.'

Furthermore, Baxendale was not overly happy about just doing a female version of an already established character. He wanted Minnie to be a total female warrior. Moonie suggested toning down some of the overt 'warrior style' in a letter dated 21st September 1953:

Regarding Minnie's dress, I think think we should cut out the shoulder straps and leave her with her striped jersey and black skirt. There isn't a great deal to be done to put things right.

Minnie's speciality became wreaking havoc on her main enemies - brash, bullying boys! Tackling crowds of them at a time, she developed a whirling punch that floored boys in their droves. This hilarious battle of the sexes set Minnie apart and gave her own identity.

And so, Minnie the Minx appeared in the comic just before Christmas, on 19th December, 1953 in issue 596. Although Baxendale was already forging ahead with changes to the Minx, like shedding the shoulder straps and aging her up from 9 to 12 years old, he had found a formula he liked and was popular with both the boys and girls, and adults, who read The Beano.

What else was happening in 1953?

We all know it was the year Minnie the Minx was created but there were a few other significant events happening in the same year.

20TH JANUARY, 1953 — Dwight D. Eisenhower was inaugurated
With his running mate, Richard Nixon, Eisenhower won the popular vote to become the 34th President of the United States.

5TH FEBRUARY, 1953 — Sugar rationing in the UK ends
Children across Britain mob the nearest sweet shops as the government de-rationed sugary treats. Might be why there was a lot of hyper children in The Beano that year!

5TH MARCH, 1953 — Death of Joseph Stalin
The Soviet leader dies after 12 years of absolute power over the USSR.

13TH APRIL, 1953 — Casino Royale is published
As well as Minnie the Minx, another legend is born as Ian Fleming publishes the first James Bond novel.

2ND JUNE, 1953 — Elizabeth was crowned Queen
God Save the Minx! Another queen besides Minnie begins her long reign on this day!

27TH JULY, 1953 — Korean War ends
After two years of conflict on the Korean Peninsular, an armistice is signed.

30TH DECEMBER, 1953 — First colour TV sets go on sale
The first colour TV sets go on sale in the US, retailing about $1,175, but in the UK the BBC didn't go full colour until 1969.

65 YEARS OF MINXING!

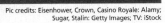

Minnie's debut in the pages of The Beano looks quite different to the minx we know today. The strip itself took up less than half a page in the comic, with the rest of the spread devoted to a prose story, Runaways with Grandad. At least one thing hasn't changed – her gift for causing trouble!

With the pages still set in monochrome, Minnie was yet to inherit her red and black colours, or her mop of auburn hair. We know from George Moonie's letters to Leo Baxendale that these were always planned should her strip prove popular enough to go to 'colour', which in 1953 meant the addition of red.

No doubt due to print deadlines and the intensity of the weekly schedule, refinements such as the removal of the shoulder straps weren't introduced until after Minnie has started appearing in the comic. Others such as Moonie's instruction to make Minnie's home 'a dwelling less fanciful and with an atmosphere of having been well used' are probably the source of the broken window and the house number – 13. Still, she made quite the impression on readers and was soon a regular fixture in the comic.

Mini Minnies

Baxendale continued to refine Minnie's distinctive look, and that of her supporting cast of parents, teachers and authority figures. In the strips on this page, we meet Minnie's mum and dad, who Moonie described in a letter dated 8th September, 1953: 'Minnie's mother is O.K. for character, but Dad is a soft-looking specimen. Can you get someone nearer the type I've sketched in Picture One – a working man in open-necked shirt, sleeves rolled, wearing braces.' With everything now in place, it was time for Minnie's adventures to really take flight…

Epic adventures

By the late 1950s, it became clear that Minnie was ready to break out of her half-page comic strips and go on escapades that could fill plenty more panels. The editor obliged – with no primed catapults needed for persuasion either – and Minnie got a full page comic strip all to herself.

These comic strips are some of the best examples of the iconic Minnie character design that Baxendale settled upon. He also started to play with the title cards, coming up with increasingly inventive ways to announce the star of the show.

THE INK BEHIND THE MINX

LEO **BAXENDALE**

Leo Baxendale was one of the greatest and most influential comic artists Britain ever produced. Working for The Beano during the 1950s and early '60s, he created a unique style that comic fans loved. It was very detailed and well-observed and completely 'over the top' for its time.

Baxendale first became interested in working for The Beano in 1952, after reading his younger brother's copy. He was particularly impressed by the new style prevalent in Davey Law's Dennis the Menace. But this was not Baxendale's first encounter with The Beano as he read the first edition in 1938, but he was not impressed by the ostrich cover star.

In 1953, Baxendale finally started his first Beano strip - Little Plum, his own creation inspired by Disney's Little Hiawatha. The facial expressions on all of his characters were hilarious in their own right. Because his artwork was so popular he was asked to take on more and more strips.

Later in 1953, Baxendale was given his second strip for The Beano... a certain Minx. Baxendale had first penned Minnie when he was living in Preston. He was persuaded by the Beano team to move to Dundee where the comic had its headquarters. This way he could work closely with the editor and writers. Baxendale especially loved the close camaraderie with the Beano staff and the lengthy, maniacal

script sessions they would hold in the office. Baxendale was always a freelance artist but now he could deliver his finished strips in person. Loving the relaxed atmosphere and general hilarity of the small office, it became his second home.

With Little Plum and Minnie the Minx in 1953, The Bash Street Kids in 1954 and The Three Bears in 1960, alongside other D.C. Thomson strips like The Banana Bunch for The Beezer, Baxendale soon found the huge workload that came from this success hard to handle. As the years wore on the constant deadlines got to him and he became disillusioned with the job he had once loved. Baxendale finished working for The Beano in 1964.

JIM PETRIE

Euan Kerr, Beano editor (left) and Jim Petrie, Beano artist (right).

In 1959, Harold Cramond took over the Beano editor's chair and he soon found himself with a dilemma. He had come to realise that Leo Baxendale would soon stop drawing Minnie the Minx, so his sights set upon a promising local art teacher by the name of Jim Petrie.

Petrie was keen to get a start in cartooning, and Cramond gave him many Minnie test scenes to illustrate with the difficult task of making the sets look like Baxendale's originals. Petrie drew them all in pencil and sent his work in to the Beano office for inspection and criticism. Cramond encouraged the budding cartoonist by telling him to fill up any blank spaces with some of his zany humour. Petrie worked well with Cramond and eventually in 1961, the experienced editor thought his pupil's work was ready to go to print. Petrie's first Minnie was a good looking single page strip, a small beginning for what was to come.

Petrie would go on to produce 2,000 weekly episodes of Minnie in his near 40-year career, and throughout those decades he worked with many different Beano staff and scriptwriters. Each writer brought their own style to the stories but Petrie handled the new challenges calmly. Two notable staff writers who wrote Minnie for Petrie were Al Bernard, who loved all-action stories, and Craig Ferguson, who used Minnie's pals more. Both wrote in different styles but both understood that Petrie craved great freedom to design the individual scenes on the double page sets - the one thing Petrie thought was crucial in getting Minnie's look right.

The vast majority of Minnie stories were drawn in black and white, colours being added later, but even so, Petrie adored colour and was a very stylish man, often dressing in very vivid clothes. So, what do you think Petrie did in his spare time? He painted abstract works in the most exciting colours to make up for the Minx's lack thereof!

Jim retired after completing his 2,000th episode of Minnie. But over the years, Petrie was a great ambassador for The Beano. He would gladly show his drawing skills at schools and conferences when asked. Everyone would marvel at his effortless style on and off the page.

TOM PATERSON

After Jim Petrie's retirement, Tom Paterson was selected as his replacement to draw Minnie the Minx. Paterson was already popular with the Beano and the Dandy staff as he drew good-looking strips for both comics.

In particular, his Calamity James strip in The Beano had a cult following. The thinking behind this appointment was that Paterson was a huge fan of Minnie's original artist, Leo Baxendale, and the hope was he would produce Minnie strips close to the originals.

Paterson had honed his Baxendale-esque cartooning style as a young boy, inspired by reading and re-reading the early Baxendale strips. As a schoolboy, such was his artistic prowess that he came to the notice of the then Dandy Editor, Albert Barnes. Barnes coached Paterson in what was required of a Dandy artist, getting the budding genius to draw and redraw the same figures until he was happy progress was being made. However, after Paterson left school,

he started drawing for Fleetway Publications, D.C. Thomson's London-based competitor... a decision that did not please Mr Barnes.

By the time he started drawing strips for The Beano in the late 1980s, Paterson was a highly regarded British cartoonist. It wasn't until 2001 that he started working weekly on Minnie. He drew the Minx for a good number of years bringing his own unique take on her character. It was now nearly 40 years since Baxendale's Minnie and, in that time, Minnie had gone through subtle changes via the pen of both the writers and artists entrusted with bringing her to life each week. Paterson finished his seven-year tenure as Minnie artist in 2008.

KEN HARRISON

In early 2008, the Minx was in trouble. The Beano's character popularity polls had flagged up that Minnie was slipping down the ratings and was not as popular with the readers as she had once been.

Then Beano editor, Euan Kerr, decided to address this by selecting Dandy

artist and classic cartoonist, Ken Harrison, to illustrate her storylines. Harrison had started off his drawing career in an advertising agency where he had to draw whatever the clients were selling – anything from underpants to suspension bridges.

With Harrison's beautiful fluid style of drawing, the stories moved along much more smoothly. His interpretation of the written scripts was top class and the stories really came to life. You didn't need speech balloons on the page to understand a Harrison strip, he told the story so well in pictures.

A lot more of the stories were based at Minnie's school and her younger teacher became a regular in the strip. Of the girl herself, only one little tweak - Minnie now wore modern trainers instead of school shoes. Even celebrity guests could now

visit Minnie's pages because among his many talents, Harrison was an excellent caricature artist.

Harrison had worked on a lot of D.C. Thomson titles and drawn many weird and wonderful strips. Sir Coward de Custard and Rah-Rah Randall from The Dandy were definitely in the weird category. He was best known, however, for drawing the magnificent Desperate Dan strips that graced the front and back covers of The Dandy for nearly two decades and continue to be featured in the Dandy annual every year.

The Beano and Dandy editorial teams both enjoyed working with Harrison enormously. He was the ultimate professional. Every drawing was classy and every page was sent in to the office, from his studio in Hull, bang on schedule.

NIGEL PARKINSON

Nigel Parkinson first drew Minnie the Minx in 1997, ghosting the style of the great Jim Petrie for a handful of issues. He also ghosted some of Tom Paterson's Minnies and he began ghosting once again when Ken Harrison took up the minxing mantle. Those three gentlemen drew in such wildly different styles, Parkinson felt well prepared to draw Minnie in whatever style the next artist had. It turned out, though, that the next artist was Parkinson himself!

The Liverpudlian artist had always found Leo Baxendale's Minnie around 1958 to 1960 to be extremely funny, and so Parkinson decided to model the mood and feel of his own run on that Baxendale era.

In recent years, Parkinson has shared the penning of the Minx with Paul Palmer. Although not the regular artist, Parkinson still draws Minnie regularly in longer strips and when she often turns up in Dennis stories in specials and annuals too.

Between 1974 and 2013, Dennis was the sole cover star of The Beano and it was a great honour for Parkinson to draw Minnie on the cover solo for the first time on the occasion of her 60th anniversary. Since then, Parkinson has drawn her on the cover quite a few times, because, remember, she's tougher than all the boys!

PAUL PALMER

A self-taught cartoonist and lifelong Beano fan, Paul Palmer first started working for D.C. Thomson in 1995, when then editor, Euan Kerr, responded to Palmer's letter and sample artwork.

Kerr gave the budding artist a page of Roger the Dodger to draw which was published later that year and from there followed work on other characters, including ghosting Ivy the Terrible for Robert Nixon. It wasn't until 2000 that Dandy Editor, Morris Heggie, gave Palmer his first regular character, Korky the Cat.

Shortly after this, Palmer drew his first Minnie the Minx, ghosting Tom Paterson's Minnie, filling in when Paterson was particularly busy. He also undertook a variety of feature pages including Joe King's Grin and Share It and a Stars In Their Eyes page, which he also wrote.

Palmer subsequently did a lot of work for the summer specials, fun-size comics and D.C. Thomson annuals but it was under Craig Graham's revamped Dandy that Paul became increasingly busy, providing comic strip artwork, scripts and puzzle pages whenever needed.

When Graham moved to The Beano, Palmer was similarly busy, writing and drawing a number of characters including the Three Bears, Les Pretend, Biffo the Bear and Dangerous Dan. This was a particularly satisfying time for Palmer, tackling comic strips he grew up with and loved.

Palmer shadowed for Nigel Parkinson's Minnie a number of times during this period and also provided scripts for the strip but it was in December of 2016 that he started his extended run on the character until he hung up his pencil in August 2018.

65 YEARS OF MINXING!

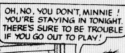

For The Beano's 50th anniversary in 1988, Minnie dressed up as Beano's first ever female character, Pansy Potter. Although she's not as strong as the 'Strong Man's Daugther', Minnie still managed to get herself into trouble!

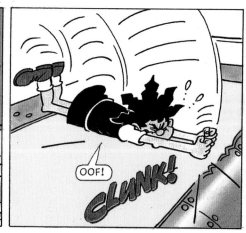

HOW TO DRAW MINNIE **THE MINX!**

'Minnie's the girl who's tougher than all the boys – and that's all the boys together! Nothing bothers her! Drawing her is a joy because you can put all that manic energy into it and it's never too much.'

Beano artist Nigel Parkinson has been drawing Minnie for over 20 years and has certainly picked up a few tricks along the way to pass on to budding artists.

1

Minnie begins with a series of simple geometric shapes – a circle for a head, rectangle for her body and a square for her skirt. It's important to get Minnie's proportions correct – her head should be approximately a quarter of her total height, while her waist should sit a little below halfway.

2

Add long rectangles and circles to mark out her arms, legs, hands and feet. Now you should have a very basic figure.

3

This is the stage when your figure will start to look like Minnie, when you add detail like her beret and bows.

5

Once you're happy with your pencil lines, draw over the top in ink. Nigel Parkinson: 'Try changing the position of her arms and legs.'

6

Rub out the pencil marks and you'll be left with your Minnie, ready for some colour.

4

With her nose in place, you can now add Minnie's expression. Nigel Parkinson: 'Try changing the expression on Minnie's face!'

7

Fill in the blacks first.

8

Add the flesh colour, reds and of course her distinctive ginger hair last! Now you've completed your Minnie, you can get her started on some serious minxing!

65
YEARS OF MINXING!

FROM SCRIPT TO COMIC

Creating a comic strip requires a lot of talent - something that the writers and artists behind Minnie have always had in spades, as they've crafted her adventures over the years with care and affection. However, it's also a time-consuming process, involving quite a few steps of collaboration to create that final comic strip. Let's take a peek behind the curtain of artist Paul Palmer's last Minnie the Minx strip for Beano and see exactly what's required to tell the story of our mischievous heroine.

STEP 1

First of all, the writer submits a script to the editorial team at Beano, who suggest edits and do that all-important laugh test to check it's up to Beano's usual standard of hilarity. This script is by Minnie writer Andy Fanton and it's a story about Minnie as a robot, titled 'Autominton'. It includes all the dialogue for the speech balloons, as well as a description of how each panel should look.

Once the script has been checked and approved, it's sent on to the Minnie artist, who reads it through and starts to plan how the story will be split up on the pages. Here, artist Paul Palmer has highlighted that panel 16 will start on the left hand side of the page.

Panel 16.
CRUNCHER flees, grossed out. FATTY turns to MIN, laughing. A voice cuts in behind him.

CRUNCHER: I'm outta here! That was GROSS!
FATTY: Nice one, Minnie!
VOICE: Thanks, Francis!

Panel 17.
PLOT TWIST! The ACTUAL MINNIE, in her usual garb, and RUBI (from RUBI'S REALLY USEFUL SCIENCE) enter, MINNIE clutching a remote control. FATTY does a double-take, amazed.

FATTY: Wait! What? This WAS a robot all along?
MIN: Yup, the AUTOMINTON 3,000! Rubi built it for me!
RUBI: I don't think Cruncher will bother anyone for a while! He got the ro-BOOT!
ROBOT MIN: CHUCKLE! CHUCKLE!

END.

STEP 2

The artist will begin to practise sketching out elements or characters in the comic strip that they don't often draw. In this case, Palmer has drawn lots of different versions of the robot Minnie, just to decide how it should look.

STEP 3

Next, it's time to draw. Like a lot of modern Beano artists, Palmer does a full line drawing in black and white, transforming Fanton's text descriptions into vibrant pictures. Palmer also makes sure that there will be space for speech balloons – they'll need to be added later.

Once the line drawing is done, Palmer then scans the drawing onto a computer, where he adds colour digitally. It's a much quicker and easier way than colouring the scene by hand.

STEP 4

Palmer sends his final coloured artwork in to the Beano team, who, using the text from the script, digitally add the speech balloons and captions into the story. The final result is the comic strip you see here, which is ready to go into Beano to be read and enjoyed by readers everywhere!

Tom Paterson was an enormously popular Beano artist, drawing Minnie's strip from 2001 - 2008. Here is his first strip from 2001, plus some of our favourites from across his time as Minnie artist.

THE MINX EFFECT

SHE'S SMART!
From her zany schemes to her cunning plans, Minnie shows that there are plenty of ways girls can use their noggin.

SHE'S FUNNY!
Minnie's always first with a funny line or joke. She can crack anyone up!

SHE'S NATURAL!
Minnie is not afraid to gurn and pull faces, showing girls they don't have to fit the mould, just to be themselves and not care what anyone thinks.

MINNIE THE MINX
- my first feminist

Minnie is a role model for young girls everywhere and for many female Beano readers, she is one of their first brushes with a girl who refuses to let anyone else define her. Over the years, Minnie's larger than life personality has made her a role model for young, rebellious girls. Here are some of the ways she is many women's first feminist icon.

SHE'S STRONG!
Who said girls can't throw? Minnie's strong enough to send furniture flying, even with her dad still sitting on it!

SHE RAISES UP OTHER GIRLS!
While Minnie is first in line to stick it to girls who tell her she's not this or that enough, when the time comes, Minnie is ready to stand side-by-side with Toots or any of the other girls against Beanotown's bullies.

SHE'S GROSS!
Some people say that girls don't sweat or women never parp. Minnie is walking, minxing proof that girls can be as stinky and gross as they want to be!

SHE BEATS THE BOYS!
Week in and week out, Minnie is always alongside or even one step ahead of the boys. (Minnie would argue it was actually three steps ahead!).

FE-**MINX**-ISM

She's 'tougher than all the boys', the 'world's wildest tomboy' and one of the most popular characters in Beano, but a lesser-known attribute Minnie the Minx boasts is her place as a feminist icon and role model.

The Minx has been waving her catapult in the face of sexism for years, shirking stereotypical female roles and femininity in favour of her own rules. Minnie doesn't wear pretty dresses, isn't tidy, meek or mild-mannered. She doesn't want to be "ladylike" or adhere to what people think conventional girls should be. Swap tea parties for skateboarding, ballet for pea-shooting, scrapbooking for scrapping – Minnie does what she wants to do, not what others think she should.

Paul Gravett, author of Great British Comics, acknowledges her influence on women in the 1950s and '60s: 'As a figure of anarchy and individualism, Minnie did inspire many women. Feminists were given a lot of encouragement to be free of male subordination.'

Minnie the Menace

I'VE BOUGHT MYSELF A BOX OF MEXICAN JUMPIN' BEANS AN' NOW ALL I'VE TO DO IS BUY SAUSAGES FOR MUM.

Minnie was not created with such lofty ideals and, in fact, Minnie was not even the first strong female created, as she was pipped to the post a whole 10 months prior on 7th February, 1953, by another black and red menace of Dandy and Topper fame, Beryl the Peril.

Beryl the Peril appeared in issue one of Topper and was already well established in its pages by the time Beano editor, George Mooney, asked Baxendale to create a female character.

Although it was not a competition, what separates the two is that Beryl is the literal incarnation of a female menace, drawn by Dennis's creator himself, Davey Law. In contrast, and in spite of her stripy jumper, Minnie has not let her association with Dennis define her, as Leo Baxendale explains in an interview from the Guardian newspaper:

'[George Moonie] wanted a female version of Dennis, which had already been done: she was called Beryl the Peril. Instead, I made Minnie the Minx into a kind of Amazonian warrior.'

Wonder Wo-Min!

The Amazons were a tribe of female warriors, fiercely strong and aggressive – their lives devoted to war. And what could be more Minnie than bruising and holding her own against scourges of bullying boys? As Baxendale states:

'I made her specialise in beating up boys – especially crowds of boys… Minnie would deliver a circular punch which would clobber two (or three) boys on its way round… Minnie even built terrible war engines with fearsome spikes for pulverising little boys.'

Even so, Minnie was struggling for an identity when Baxendale decided she should become like an Amazon.

Of course, the most famous comic book depiction of an Amazonian, and a fellow feminist icon is Wonder Woman. However, it is a different strong woman that Leo Baxendale took inspiration from – Pansy Potter the Strongman's Daughter.

As Beano's first ever female character, Baxendale was told to study Pansy Potter strips. Baxendale considered the strips to be well drawn but too old fashioned. Unlike Pansy and other comics at the time, he wanted Minnie not to 'have special powers, or superhuman strength - she was just a sturdy 12-year-old girl. She had will and ambition.'

And that's what's made Minnie so enduring. While a girl with super-strength isn't that relatable, Minnie is such a good role model because she's just a wilful little girl who stands up for her rights and who shows other little girls they can too.

ROLE MODEL

Little Minxes

Let's hear from the generation of girls that Minnie is inspiring!

Amelia Brogden from Singapore:

'I like Minnie the Minx because she is just like me and I'm also tougher than all the boys. She inspires me to beat the boys in the school because some of them say they think boys are better than girls at running BUT I beat them every time.'

Violet from County Armagh:

'She gets into lots of mischief and she is the coolest in the comic. She's a bit like me — she likes some types of books and doesn't mind getting dirty for fun, she is forced to do ballet by her dad and she could easily stop being a tomboy any time she wants to. She gets into scrapes but always manages to get out of trouble, but mostly because she's tougher than all the boys!'

Lola from Hartlepool:

'Minnie has inspired me to write my own minxing magazine and come up with a 'Minx or Menace club' at school! I think she's cool because she's a girl with attitude, she's crazy and she's good fun just like me!'

Grown-up Minxes

Young minxes have grown up but they remain inspired by what Minnie meant to them.

'I wasn't as brave as she was but I did respect her standing up to authority. She's a bit of a rebel!'
Artist, Sarah Millman

'She was a tomboy which I very much was, and still am, so it was nice to have a girl character beating up all the boys in the comic! It was like, oh good, there's a girl kicking butt.'
Artist and writer, Jess Bradley

'She never saw herself as being worse than the boys and she didn't let the fact that she was a girl stop her from doing anything. She's such a strong role model and she doesn't let her gender define what she can and can't do. She does what she wants!'
Rubi's Screwtop Science artist, Emily McGorman-Bruce

'She doesn't worry about being a good girl. Historically, female characters on TV or in comics have been the sensible ones who stand by tutting while the guys do crazy things. Not Min - she's always been right there in the thick of any mayhem. She's that unpredictable friend who makes your life more fun.'
Beano and Dandy artist, Laura Howell

For over six decades, Minnie the Minx has proven and cemented her place as a feminist role model and icon - rousing girls, women, and even boys to push beyond what society expects of them. No doubt, she'll continue inspiring for another 65 years…

FAMOUS FACES

Wayne Rooney

Chris Evans

As we've seen, Minnie the Minx has had a massive impact on popular culture, but what happens when popular culture strikes back? A number of famous faces have appeared with Minnie, though none have escaped a good minxing for doing so.

Beano No. 3,000 was a celebrity-packed special, which saw Geri Halliwell join Minnie to salute the milestone!

In 2010, Minnie embarked on a mission to get famous (well, more famous) by taking her own brand of mischief on a tour of the pop culture of the time…

Geri Halliwell

Cheryl Cole

Jamie Oliver

And a host of Eastenders characters!

While her attempts to find fame faltered, she'll always be one of Beano's superstars!

MADE OF BRONZE

If you go down to Dundee city square today, you're likely to see a very famous scene. Cast in bronze stands an 8-foot-tall Desperate Dan striding out with his faithful canine companion, Dawg. Not so far behind, stalking and taking aim at Dan's rear-end with her trusty catapult is none other than one Minnie the Minx.

Originally the scene was supposed to just be Minnie taking a pot-shot at Dan but as the huge bronze cowboy needed more stability Dan's dog was added as a support. As such, while the desperado strides on oblivious, it is the mighty mutt who is the one eyeballing Minnie's attack. Watch how you go, girl!

Unveiled in 2001 by a team of Dundee school children, the sculptures were the work of artists, Tony and Susie Morrow, and cost a heavy £45,000 at the time. Since then, it has been visited by celebrities like Danny Wallace and even the Olympic torch in 2012. It celebrates two of Dundee's most recognised citizens and the city's status as a national comic creating centre.

The Minnie sculpture and Desperate Dan at their location in Dundee's city centre.

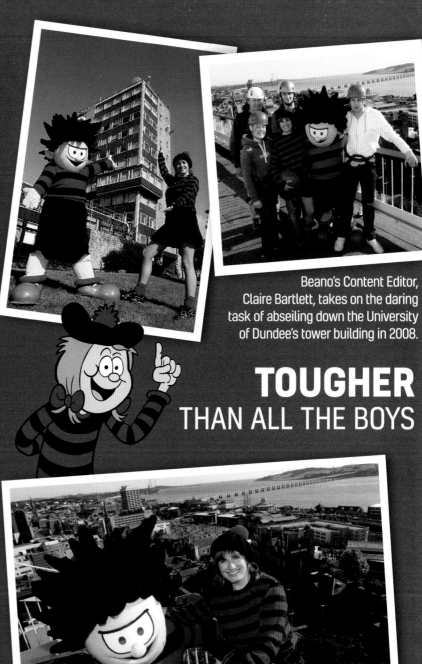

Beano's Content Editor, Claire Bartlett, takes on the daring task of abseiling down the University of Dundee's tower building in 2008.

TOUGHER
THAN ALL THE BOYS

To celebrate 70 years of Beano, the comic decided to raise money for kids' charity, CLIC Sargent - a charity dedicated to helping children with cancer and their families. Readers were sponsored to cause as much mischief as possible during Gnashtional Menace Day on the 30th July, 2008, by telling jokes and pulling pranks. All sponsorship money was donated to CLIC Sargent.

Minnie's tagline in today's comic is, 'She's tougher than all the boys' and this was exhibited in a case of life imitating art when

the then only female member of the editorial team, Claire Bartlett decided to raise more money for the charity by abseiling down Dundee University's Tower Block dressed as the feisty minx herself. The male staff were all too scared!

Dennis was there at the top to encourage Claire... and give her a helpful shove when she faltered during those first few tentative steps on the way down!

140 feet later and Minnie proved once more that Beano girls really are tougher than all the boys!

YEARS OF
MINXING!

THOROUGHLY MODERN MINX

COVER STAR!

Beano No. 3715, celebrating 60 years of Minnie the Minx.

Minnie's popularity over the years was such that in the early 1980s it was proposed that Minnie should spin off into her own comic much like The Bash Street Kids' Plug had a few years before.

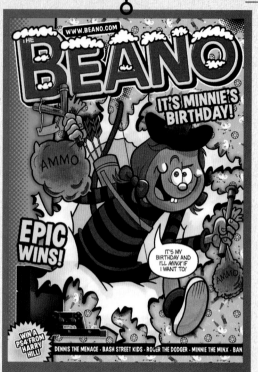

Although her next cover appearance didn't come until 4th February, 2017, it proved no less successful, as it was shortlisted for Cover of the Year at Scotland's Professional Publishers Association Awards.

Its success proved that Minnie could hold her own as a cover star and the result can be seen in the gallery on the next page.

This is the cover that was created by Jim Petrie, which has never been seen publically before. Although the comic never launched, the work that was done for it was not wasted and went on to appear in The Beano Book 1985.

It was twenty years later on 11th December, 2013, that Minnie the Minx finally pushed Dennis and Gnasher off the cover for the first time since 1974! Not only was this the first time in nearly 40 years this had happened, in doing so Minnie became the first female cover star too! It was a fitting way to mark Minnie's 60th anniversary in the comic.

65 YEARS OF MINXING!

Today Minnie is a regular fixture on the cover, and her popularity has helped to pave the way for new female characters in the comic such as JJ and Rubi from TV series Dennis & Gnasher: Unleashed, and Betty & the Yeti, who all appear in the comic every week! Not bad, Minnie. Not bad at all!

2018 was Beano's 80th birthday, but it's also proved to have been the 'Year of the Minx' as well!

A Paul Palmer Minnie from March, 2018, showing our favourite Minx getting the better of Soppy Susan the haughty girl next door who is forever looking down on Minnie.

MINNIE THE MINX

SHE'S TOUGHER THAN ALL THE BOYS...

WORDS: ANDY FANTON ART: PAUL PALMER

 Who is the most powerful potato in the galaxy? Darth Tater!

Laura Howell

Following the departure of Paul Palmer as regular Minnie artist, the opportunity arose for a new cartoonist to take on the prestigious role. Enter Laura Howell, a long time Beano contributor. Like Minnie, she's been a pioneer in breaking conventions, becoming the first ever female Beano artist in 2007. It's fitting that she's now collaborating with Beano's first female cover star in telling a host of hilarious, minx-tastic stories.

Howell began her professional career working as an editor in children's publishing, before bursting into the comics industry after inking Hunt Emerson's Beano strip Ratz.

Then-Beano editor Alan Digby took notice, and commissioned her first Beano strip titled 'Johnny Bean from Happy Bunny Green'. It followed the titular character, an anarchic boy with a penchant for trouble, as he caused endless strife for the residents of a sleepy village.

As Howell describes the strip, it 'used the concept of something that looked cute but had a spiky edge!'

Since then, Howell has drawn plenty of well-known Beano characters, including Little Plum, Les Pretend and Ivy the Terrible. She was also the artist for the revival of Beanotown prankster Tricky Dicky in 2013.

This next step is an exciting one for Howell, who has always had a personal affection for Minnie, describing her as 'that unpredictable friend who makes your life more fun'.

She is also aware of the responsibility that she's inheriting, stressing that 'It's important to do justice to both her artistic heritage and also keep the readers happy. I never lose sight of the fact that I used to be one of them, so I try to stay focused on what would have made me laugh – and still does!' From all at Beano, congratulations and welcome to the Minx Club!

See Laura Howell's test strip that convinced the Beano team that she was the right choice...

MINNIE THE MINX
SHE'S TOUGHER THAN ALL THE BOYS....

MINX-SPIRATION

As a comics' icon, Minnie has inspired plenty of young readers to pick up a pencil and draw their own colourful likeness of her. This continues today - if the busy postbox of the Beano office is anything to go by - with the Beano team still sifting through plenty of unique drawings of Minnie every week.

Some of those young Beano readers would go on to become brilliant artists in their own right, forging careers whilst creating their own spirited characters, or capturing the faces of famous figures. We've asked four talented female artists for their own take on the undisputed queen of British comics - each as unique as the Minx herself.

Emily McGorman-Bruce

McGorman-Bruce is a familiar face at Beano, responsible for drawing Rubi and Pie Face in the weekly comic. Becoming one of the artists in the comic has been a dream of hers since she first started reading Beano at the age of eight – something that she can verify, having written that exact occupation down as her dream job during a primary school class assignment!

Minnie was always one of her favourite faces in Beano as a kid, and McGorman-Bruce even made a foray into cosplay with a red and black stripy jumper, knitted by a neighbour. She's well aware of the impact of the iconic character, describing her as a 'strong role model', who 'doesn't let her gender define what she can and can't do.'

Jess Bradley

When it comes to weird and wonderful stories, Bradley is never short of ideas. She began her work in the comic industry through self-publishing her own imaginative comics, and often provides illustrations for kids' books and magazines. Bradley is also a contributor to Beano, penning scripts for Dennis's menace hounds, Gnasher and Gnipper, as well as Tricky Dicky.

Beano was always in Bradley's house from a young age, and she would share the annual with her brother every year. A self-professed tomboy, she liked to see a character that wasn't a girly stereotype, but tough and independent. Like Minnie's self-possessed approach to life, Bradley now inspires minx-like confidence in the next generation of young artists with school workshops, where her most frequent advice is 'don't compare yourself to other people - just draw to the best of your ability.'